Mr King is trapped in the shower!

"I know what to do!" he says.

He asks Mr Summerday to help.

Mr Summerday looks at the plan.

They try the shower.

Oh no!

"I know what to do," says
Mr Summerday.

He asks Mrs Macdonald to help.

Mrs Macdonald looks at the plan.

"Now we can try it."

It works!

They all get a shower!